FOR THE LOVE OF
DOG!

FOR THE LOVE OF
DOG!

JOHN DONEGAN

DOG ALMIGHTY!
DOG HELP US!
FOR DOG'S SAKE!

CHANCELLOR PRESS

Dog Almighty! first published in 1986 by Souvenir Press Limited
Dog Help Us! first published in 1987 by Souvenir Press Limited
For Dog's Sake! first published in 1990 by Souvenir Press Limited

This edition first published in 1994 by Chancellor Press
an imprint of Reed Consumer Books Limited
Michelin House, 81 Fulham Road, London SW3 6RB
and Auckland, Melbourne, Singapore and Toronto

ISBN 1 85152 656 0

A CIP catalogue record for this book is available from the British Library

Printed and bound in Slovakia
by Aventinum
51711

Some of the cartoons in this book have previously
appeared in *Punch* and are reproduced by
kind permission of the proprietors, Punch Publications Ltd.

CONTENTS

DOG
ALMIGHTY!

'It doesn't have to grab you — just eat it!'

'Why wait till Father's Day? Give it to him now.'

'Stand perfectly still! One false move and he'll faint.'

'He's not always so friendly with total strangers, but then he's not always drunk.'

'There's a furry thing in here eating cheese. I understand
that's your department.'

'Clear off, or I'll set my stockbroker on you.'

'Yes, yes, I'm yours, body and soul! Now can I watch Clive James?'

'Merciful Heaven, Winston! Where *did* you learn to tango like that?'

'Do I hear the merry clink of ice on Waterford?'

'Kill!'

'Would you mind if Rocky and I discussed this alone, Arthur?'

'Go and see what's bothering him. He doesn't usually howl for nothing.'

'Margaret thinks it makes him look dependable.'

'He's very gentle, but prey to uncontrollable fits of the giggles.'

'Contrary to popular mythology, I never actually said "Play it again, Sam".'

'You're kidding! Just that and they *feed* you!'

'. . . and finally a word from Lloyd on security.'

'Here's the fifty thousand. Now hand over the cat.'

'No, you may *not* be tried by twelve good dogs and true.'

'So I'm hypnotised. So what?'

'My God, you'd better go! He'll be home any minute.'

'Don't be silly, Tarquin. Nobody elopes any more.'

'Mac's the name, thirty-two pounds of lightning reaction and compact muscle.
I don't scare easy or suffer fools gladly. Remember that and
we'll all have a nice time.'

'Okay, but be quick about it!'

'Negotiate? What is there to negotiate?'

'Go ahead, organise a union. I'll organise the new potatoes, the garden peas and the mint sauce.'

'Well, of *course* I'm surprised — I'm usually ignored at parties.'

'It's amazing! You look so small on television.'

'You see? He's a different dog when he smiles.'

'Well, I've been in three or four documentaries, two feature films, and loads of commercials, of course. Mostly as a dog.'

'For Heaven's sake! Pay it, or make a scene. One or the other.'

'The fact is, Leonard, I'm not your real father.'

'More colour, more! He likes lots and lots of colour.'

'*Must* you go home? Why not stay the night?'

'I still say it's unusual for a spaniel to leave home.'

'. . . and a sausage and a small scotch for him.'

'The usual? I serve six hundred drinks a day and I'm supposed to remember "the usual"?'

'You don't *look* eighteen.'

'Wouldn't have such a thing as a swizzle stick, I suppose?'

'That's Marcus in his prime — proud, arrogant and top of the heap, yet
tenderness itself with his loved ones. I forget who the man is.'

DOG

HELP US!

'Call of the Wild be damned! I need the money.'

'Margaret! Do we want anyone savaged?'

'Could you be a little more precise than "Yuk!"?'

'A duel?!'

'Just a suggestion — try both barrels with your eyes shut.'

'Oh, nothing really. Just a spot of fishing.'

'...and to round off a truly dazzling display, a Victory Roll!'

'Oh, terrific. Fell into a ditch, pulled a muscle, got a cold, no sympathy, no rabbits, and no lunch. How about you?'

'Oh, I don't mind. Chasseur, Bordelaise, au poivre, Tartare — or just plain grilled.'

'It's nothing to do with your regional accent. There just aren't any jobs
around.'

'Put it this way. He runs the place, but I have a controlling interest.'

'All the panache and savoir faire you can muster, Angelo. Something tells me
he's from the Food Guide.'

'I'll stick to mineral water. Some of us have work to do.'

'Hey, that's pretty good! "Work is the curse of the drinking classes". I wish I'd said that.'

'Step aside, please. I happen to be a sheepdog.'

'You must be new around here. When I say "Climb that tree", you climb that tree!'

'I'll say it once more — just hop back onto the road and there won't be any trouble.'

'Well, I used to be in the poultry business, but I got sick of picking up dead birds.'

'Okay, but if he's sick you'll have to clean it up.'

'. . . and no drinking in the kennels. Two weeks' holiday, every other Sunday off, and all the foxes you can eat. Next!'

'I hope you're not squeamish. They tend to puke without warning.'

'What's cruel about it? They don't feel a thing.'

'Strictly speaking, I should, with one swift slash of razor-like fangs, disembowel you, but what the hell — it's Sunday.'

'*Really*, darling! I'm opening the damn thing.'

'Years of sacrifice, and now you want to be a sheepdog?!'

'Be sensible, Kelvin! You can't be my best friend *and* my agent.'

'Police. Open up.'

'Now think very carefully — did you show the accused your warrant card
before or after you threw him down the stairs?'

'I don't mind scaring the hell out of them, but have you ever *tasted* one?'

'Are you kidding?'

'. . . looked round and he'd gone. He's about five ten, pink nose, shiny black coat, answers to the name of Wally, and keeps falling over.'

'I don't fancy yours much.'

'Oh, God! Not another party political broadcast!'

'Of course he isn't very frisky! The poor little chap's over-fed and under-exercised!'

'I know the feeling. I'm not gregarious either.'

'No thanks! *You* kill it.'

'Mind if we sit this

? Their cat's a bit dodgy.'

'Speaking strictly as a friend, Des, I don't see how you can expect them to promote you when you spend half your day in here.'

'"Listen," I said, "if you'd been chasing stupid sheep around in the rain instead of tarting yourself up all day," I said, "*you'd* leave mud all *over* the place, never mind a bit on the carpet." "Well," she sayd, all toffee-nosed, "*I* like to keep myself nice, but if I *was* daft enough to get dirty," she says, "at least I wouldn't have to be put in the bath and washed like a big baby," she says, and walks off. Cats!'

'All clear both ways, but don't take all day over it.'

'But I *don't* hate you! I love you, we all love you, and I swear I won't call you
"Dopey", or yell at you, or embarrass you in any way ever again, and you can
be in the trials squad if you want to, but only if you want to . . .'

'Because I'm great and you're small, that's why.'

FOR
DOG'S
SAKE!

'You're not making things any easier for me, Monty.'

'It's The Wild again.'

'... and this time, don't feign a limp, don't chew his stethoscope, and don't call him "Doc".'

'. . . and don't fall for all that "Best Friend" stuff. We're just another investment.'

'Nothing to it. Just keep showing them how, then, one day, *you* throw it.'

'If the Good Lord had meant me to run He would have given me a tracksuit.'

'I've never called anyone "Sir" and I don't intend to start now.'

'Never mind "Pourquoi?" Just fetch it.'

'They're identical, except that one says "Potato" and the other says "Potahto".'

'Well, can I have the bit you're *not* reading?'

'You're as near to it as I am — you fill 'em up.'

'For pity's sake, Max, it's only the postman!'

'You're an eco-system and I'm an eco-system. Anything that has fleas
is an eco-system.'

'White cat speak with forked tongue.'

'I warn you — I don't take prisoners.'

'It certainly *is* my business! I happen to be an ornithologist.'

'For once I agree with you — it's an improvement.'

'Oh, I *do* beg your pardon. I didn't know it was leg-licking time.'

'Listen to him, dear. He's trying to tell you something terribly important.'

'Eventually, of course, one was forced to the inevitable conclusion that,
for all practical purposes, barking is a dead language.'

'The accused will confine his answers to "Yes" or "No".'

'Look, if it makes you feel any better, *I'll* forget *your* birthday.'

'It's high time we had his claws clipped. I can't take much more of that
tap-dancing.'

'I think you should have a word with him, Douglas. He wants to have his ears pierced.'

'Any chance of a drink while I'm waiting?'

'Well, *we* like it with garlic and herbs'

'Closer, please. Just a little closer.'

'Sorry to interrupt, but who the hell *is* that?'

'How many times do I have to tell you, Trixie? Don't ring me at home!'

'Hold on: you-know-who wants to say "Hello".'

'Turn that down, or take it up to your room!'

'Goodnight, Gus. Thanks for letting me stay up late.'

'By the authority invested in me by Cwm Valley Farm I must ask you
to proceed down to the far end of the field in an orderly manner, there
to disperse and go about your business pending further instructions. In
short — move it.'

'Don't push your luck, stupid. One taste of blood and I'll be sick.'

'*You're* typecast? What about me?'